GRADE **2** TWO

POWERTHINK

Cooperative Critical Thinking Activities

Written by Anita Reith Stohs

Illustrated by Becky J. Radtke

Editor: Hanna Otero

Cover Design: Kristin Lock

Graphic Artists: Danielle Dela Cruz and Anthony Strasburger

FS112111 POWERTHINK—Grade Two
All rights reserved-Printed in the U.S.A.
Copyright ©2000 Frank Schaffer Publications
23740 Hawthorne Blvd., Torrance, CA 90505

Table of Contents

INTRODUCTION

"There are one-story intellects, two-story intellects and three-story intellects with skylights. All fact collectors who have no aim beyond their facts are one-story people. Two-story people compare, reason, generalize, using the labor of the fact collectors as their own. Three-story people idealize, imagine, predict – their best illumination comes from above through the skylight."

Oliver Wendell Holmes

As educators, our goal is to assist students to become "third-story thinkers." Both the National Council of Teachers of Mathematics and the National Science Teachers Association recommend including problem solving and decision making as major goals of education.

What is critical thinking? Research indicates that the skill most basic to critical thinking is the ability to listen or read actively while continuously analyzing the information being presented. Sounds pretty basic, doesn't it? This ability requires the learner to be able to engage in an internal dialogue. Effective learners can dialogue internally without skipping steps.

Current recommendations suggest that children can best learn critical thinking skills by working in small groups or pairs. Working in pairs forces students to externalize their thinking – to think aloud, and to identify errors and skipped steps. It also teaches students to recognize and edit unsystematic thinking in themselves and others.

The **POWERTHINK** series of reproducible activity sheets is designed to provide cooperative learning opportunities for either small groups or pairs. There are six levels of challenge in the **POWERTHINK** series, allowing you to introduce critical thinking material at a sequential pace.

This **POWERTHINK** book provides you with activity sheets that pertain to the major content areas of language arts, social studies, mathematics, science, art, and problem solving.

Levels 1, 2, and 3 of the **POWERTHINK** series are designed clearly and simply:

 The Power Play symbol indicates the directions to the students. The icon shows two students working together, but small groups of three will work in many cases.

 The Lightning Strike icon indicates extended activities to guide your students to further observations or academic destinations.

 Under the dashed line on each activity sheet you will find the Power Up icon. These are the author's comments and directions to the educator on how to prepare the children for the activity. When you're ready to make copies of the activity sheets for your students, simply fold back on the dashed lines and this section will not appear on your student copies.

The teaching of critical thinking skills can also be a forum for truly individual positive reinforcement, so on page 63 you will find a list of powerful verbal reinforcers. Use these to encourage your students to become "**POWERTHINKERS.**"

Happy **POWERTHINKING!**

WHAT'S WRONG HERE?

Power Play

1. Look at each set of pictures. Put an **X** on the item that does not belong.
2. Tell why it does not belong.

 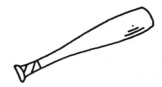 

The _____ does not belong because _____

The _____ does not belong because _____

The _____ does not belong because _____

The _____ does not belong because _____

Lightning Strike!

Happy…Smile…Frown…Laugh: Which word does not belong? Explain your answer.
Take turns with your partner drawing groups of pictures or writing words and finding the one that does not belong.

Power Up!

Part of learning to categorize involves being able to distinguish between similar and different functions. Encourage the students to look for patterns of similar usage as they find the one item in each row that does not belong.

KEYS TO WHAT?

Power Play

Look at the keys in the bag. Trace them onto the paper below. Tell what you think each key is used for.

Key #1	Key #2	Key #3	Key #4

I think key #1 is used to _____.

I think key #2 is used to _____.

I think key #3 is used to _____.

I think key #4 is used to _____.

Lightning Strike

1. Do a crayon rubbing of each key. Draw what the key is opening.
2. Sort many keys into different piles.
3. Trace a key and call it the "magic key." Write or draw a picture about how to use it.
4. Compare a key with a computer password. How are they alike? How are they different?

- -

Power Up!

Much can be deduced about an object's function by simply observing it. Encourage children to look at each key's size, shape, material, and whether there are any words or markings.

- As a group, brainstorm things that can be opened or turned on with a key. For example: car ignition, bicycle lock, jewelry box.
- Provide each group with a zip-lock bag of four keys. Try to provide keys to a variety of locks: car, door, jewelry box, suitcase, etc.

HOW ARE THEY ALIKE?

Power Play

Look at the pictures below. How are they alike?
1. Circle things that could be red.
2. Put an **X** on things that could be green.
3. Color the things that are alive.
4. Draw a box around things that have round parts.

Lightning Strike!

Many things fit into more than one group. Can you think of another group name for two or more of these things? Make a list of things that could be yellow.

- -

Power Up!

This activity helps students learn that not everything fits into one neat category as they look for similarities between unlike objects. Before starting this activity, name an object and ask students to think of several categories for it. For example: an airplane could be a type of transportation, something that flies, something silver, something large, and something fun.

WHAT WOULD YOU CHOOSE?

Power Play

Behind the door is a large box. Nobody knows what's in the box. In the chest is $1,000. You may have the $1,000 or what's in the box.

1. Talk with your partner about the choices. Agree on which one you would rather have.

2. What did you decide to take?_____

3. Why did you make that choice?_____

Lightning Strike!

What would you do with $1,000? List some of the things that might be in the box. Draw a picture of what you think would be in the box.

- -

Power Up!

Decisions are not easy, especially when one of the options involves unknowns. Talk about some types of decisions students make every day like what to wear, what to do, what to eat, what to watch on TV, what books to read. Ask them to vocalize the steps they go through mentally to make decisions.

- Ask students to describe a difficult decision they have had to make.

AND THEN?

Power Play

1. Look at the first two words in each row.
2. On the blank line, write a word that could come next in the sequence.
3. In the box above each word, draw a picture to illustrate the word.

tiny	average	_____
short	medium	_____

Lightning Strike!

Use your imagination and complete the sequence below. Draw pictures and write one or two words to explain your sequence.

_____	_____	_____

Power Up!

In this activity, students complete sequences and illustrate the words with examples. They are then asked to write and illustrate a complete sequence of their own. Before starting, ask students to finish these sequences: fast, faster, _____; first, second, _____; good, better, _____.

SUPER SPOON

Power Play

1. What can you eat with a spoon? Inside the outline write some of the things you can eat with a spoon.
2. Is there anything you can't eat with a spoon? Write some of these things outside the spoon.
3. Compare your list with your partner's.

Things I cannot eat with a spoon...

Things I can eat with a spoon...

Lightning Strike!

Now that you've thought about things you can eat with a spoon, think about some ways you could use a Super Spoon. Could you use it to dig a hole? Carry water? Shoot rubber bands? Make a list of all the wild and wonderful uses for a Super Spoon.

Power Up!

• Thinking about how everyday objects are used is the purpose of this activity. Invite students to look at a spoon in terms of how it can and cannot be used. This is a brainstorming activity, so remind them that the sky's the limit!

• As an option, provide each group with a spoon.

WHAT'S FOR DINNER?

Power Play

1. It's dinner time, but something is missing from each plate! Find what is missing and draw it on each plate. (One way to do this is to compare two plates at a time to see what each plate is missing.)

2. What foods should be on a full plate? Draw them in.

Lightning Strike!

Each square below has a section with a dot in it. Color each one of these sections a different color. If each one of these sections was a part of a larger square, what would the larger square look like? Color the larger square to show how it would look.

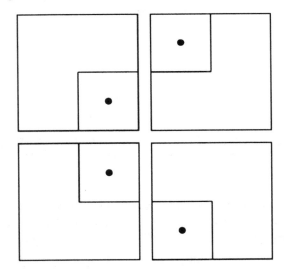 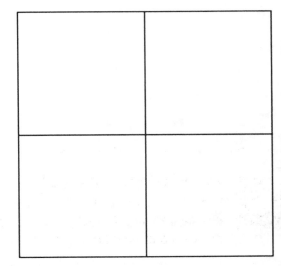

Power Up!

Determining whole-part relationships is a process calling for a variety of higher-level thinking skills. This activity encourages children to compare incomplete groups and reason deductively to arrive at the contents of the complete group.

FLOWER PUZZLER

Power Play

1. Look at the three flowers and the three stems.
2. How many ways can you put them together? Draw all the different plants you can make.
3. Talk with your partner about how to figure out the number of different plants you could make with three flowers and three stems.

Draw as many combinations as you can below...

Lightning Strike!

Make up a "parts puzzle" for your partner to put together. You might draw trees and trunks or mushrooms and stems.

Power Up!

The goal of this activity is to encourage students to think about all the flower combinations in a systematic way. For example, a child might report her thinking this way: "I took the daisy flower and matched it with the first stem, then the second stem, and then the third stem. Then I did the same thing with the rose and the tulip. I found out that there are nine types of plants I could make."

- Use three blocks to demonstrate the different ways they can be stacked together in sets of two.

| A | B | C |

A	A	B	B	C	C
B	C	C	A	A	B

WHAT MAKES THEM SIMILAR?

Power Play

1. Look at the pictures and read the words below the pictures.
2. Discuss and decide how the two pairs on each line are related.
3. Write about how they are related on the lines below the pictures.

 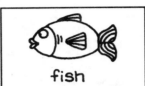 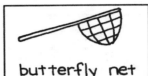 

| fishing pole | fish | butterfly net | butterfly |

_____

_____

  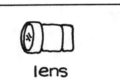 

| eye | person | lens | camera |

_____

_____

   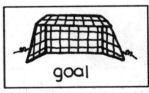

| basketball | hoop | soccer ball | goal |

_____

_____

Lightning Strike!

With your partner, write your own pairs of related pictures and share them with the class.

- -

Power Up!

Understanding analogies is a critical thinking skill that will transfer to all content areas in the curriculum. These pictorial representations are a good beginning to understanding verbal analogies.

FS112111 POWERTHINK

Frank Schaffer Publications

PICTURE DETECTIVE

Power Play

Look at the pictures in the boxes. Only two objects can be found in all four boxes.

1. Talk with your partner about different ways to find the two pictures that are in all the boxes.
2. Pick one of the ways you thought of and describe it below.

_____

_____

_____

3. Find the two objects that are in all four boxes. What are they?

_____ and _____.

Lightning Strike!

Problems can often be solved in more than one way. Think of another problem that could be solved in many ways. List the problem and some ways to solve it.

Power Up!

Students need to learn to approach problems from different angles. This activity allows students to explore possible ways to determine the two objects that appear in all four boxes. After students complete this activity, ask them to share their different approaches with the class.

Answer: The rabbit and the tulip appear in all four boxes.

WHAT NEXT?

Power Play
1. Look at each set of pictures. Draw a picture of what will happen next.
2. Share your drawings with your partner.

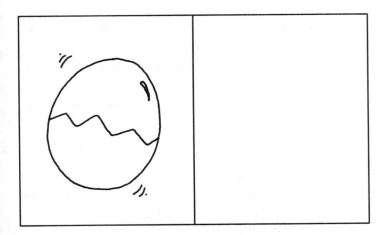

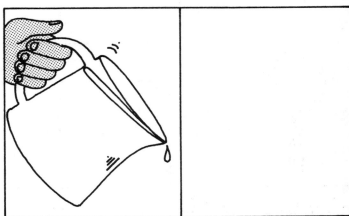

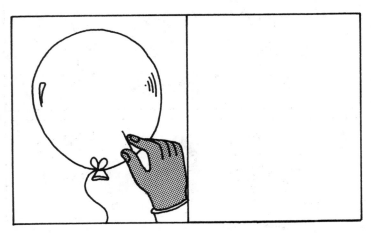

Lightning Strike!
1. Draw a picture of something happening. Have your partner draw what will happen next.
2. Read a story to your partner. Stop at different places in the story and have your partner guess what will happen next. Do the same with a story that your partner reads to you.

Power Up!
One of the important critical thinking skills is the ability to see patterns and predict what will happen next. This activity encourages students to look at what has happened already in order to predict what is likely to happen next.

WISH UPON A *STAR*

Power Play

1. What if you could wish upon a star and your wish would come true? Make a list of things you might wish for.

_____   _____

_____   _____

_____   _____

2. Pick one thing from your list to write or draw inside the star.

3. Why did you choose what you did?_____

_____

4. Share your answer with your partner.

Lightning Strike!

1. Cut out star-shaped pages and make a wishing book.
2. What would you wish for someone else? Make a wishing star to show your wish for them.

- -

Power Up!

An important part of critical thinking is learning to make independent judgments, based upon one's own preferences. Have students cut out the stars and use them as decorations in the classroom.

MIXED-UP TITLES

Power Play

These book titles got all mixed up. See if you can write them in the right order.

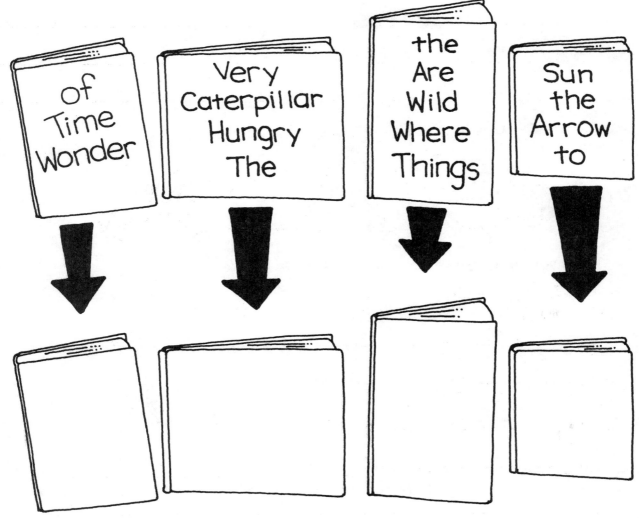

Lightning Strike!

Take turns mixing up words for titles of books that you have read in your class. Have someone else put them together again.

- -

Power Up!

Use a book title familiar to the students to demonstrate how to put words back in the right order.
Example: Clown The God of → The Clown of God.

Answer Key: 1. *Time of Wonder* 2. *The Very Hungry Caterpillar* 3. *Where the Wild Things Are* 4. *Arrow to the Sun*

ALPHABET SOUP

Power Play

1. When Luis tried to make "stone soup," the alphabet letters to the words "stone soup" fell into the pot too. Can you find them?

Write the letters in their correct order below.

___ ___ ___ ___ ___   ___ ___ ___ ___

2. How many different words can you make out of the letters?

_____   _____   _____

_____   _____   _____

_____   _____   _____

_____   _____   _____

_____   _____   _____

3. Compare your list with another group. See how many different words the whole class found.

Lightning Strike!

Think of another book title or name of a character. How many different words can you make from the letters in those words?

- -

Power Up!

- Read <u>Stone Soup</u> by Marcia Brown (New York: Scribner, 1947).
- Tell the children that putting different letters together to make words is like putting together an alphabet "stone soup."

Answer Key: net, nest, no, noose, nose, not, note, nut, on, one, open, oust, out, pen, pet, pest, poet, pone, pose, posse, post, pot, pout, pun, pus, put, sent, set, snoop, snoot, snout, so, son, soon, soot, spent, spot, spoon, spout, step, stoop, stop, store, sue, sun, sup, ten, to, too, ton, tone, top, toss, tune, up, use

YOU'RE MY HERO!

Power Play

1. With a partner, use the worksheet below to make up your own folk-tale hero.
2. After you finish the worksheet, use it and your imagination to make up a story about your folk hero.

Name	Age
Occupation	Hometown
Special tools or equipment	
Friends or companions	
Favorite food	**Draw a picture**
Best quality	
Worst quality	
Favorite song	
What he or she can do that no one else can	
Unusual characteristics	
Greatest fear	
Best kind of day	

Power Up!

- Review stories of folk-tale heroes, such as Pecos Bill, Paul Bunyun, John Henry, and Johnny Appleseed.
- Supply pencils and crayons for each group.

FROM UGLY TO LOVELY

Power Play

1. Cut out the chain links below.
2. Find the chain links that go first and last.
3. On the other links, draw pictures of what happened in the middle of the story. If you need to, cut more links to use.
4. Glue each tab under a link to make a chain.

Lightning Strike!

Use chain link pictures to tell other stories you have read.

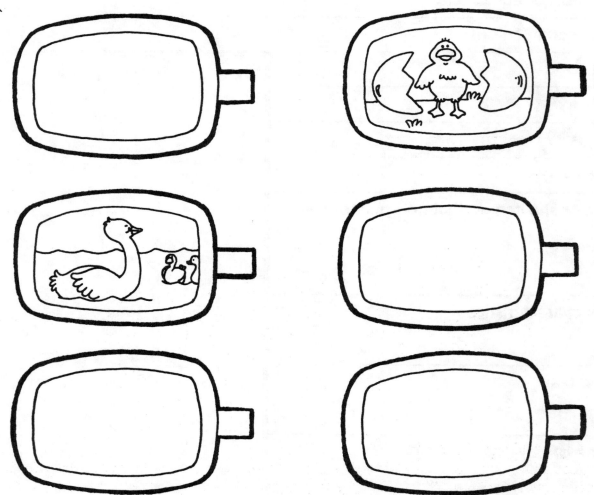

Power Up!

- Review the story "The Ugly Duckling" by Hans Christian Andersen.
- Talk about how different parts of a story are like links in a chain.
- Provide each group with crayons and scissors.

COULD A DOG DO THAT?

Power Play

1. With a partner, take turns reading your book. Look for what is real and what is not real about the animal in the book.
2. List some of the real and not real things the animal does.

Name of Book: _____

Name of Animal: _____

Things the Animal Does

Real	Not Real
_____	_____
_____	_____
_____	_____
_____	_____
_____	_____
_____	_____

> Would I really do that?

Lightning Strike!

Read a fairy or folk tale. Talk about what is real and what is not real in the story. Why do authors put in parts that are not real? Does it make the story better or worse?

Power Up!

- Select a children's book about an animal to read to the class. Talk about whether or not a real animal would do what the animal in the book does.
- Provide each group with a children's book about an animal.

RAINING GUMDROPS AND MARSHMALLOWS

Power Play

1. Have you ever heard someone say, "It's raining cats and dogs?" Talk with your partner about what that means.

2. What else could you say that would mean it was raining very hard? Write some ideas below.

   It's raining _____ and _____

   It's raining _____ and _____

   It's raining _____ and _____

3. If it was raining softly, maybe you could say, "It's raining rose petals and cotton candy." What else could you say if it was raining very gently?

   It's raining _____ and _____

Lightning Strike!

What would be the best things that it could be raining? Gumdrops and jelly beans? Quarters and cotton candy? Write the best one you can think of.
Draw a picture of a rainy day when something comes from the sky besides rain.

Power Up!

This activity encourages students to think about phrases they may have heard and explore what the phrases mean. Then they have an opportunity to write some new ones of their own.

- Use some common phrases and ask students to explain what they mean: A stitch in time saves nine. A watched pot never boils. Haste makes waste. A penny saved is a penny earned.

POSTCARD FROM BOOKLAND

Power Play

1. Cut out the postcard.
2. Pick a character from a book you have read. Write a postcard that the character could send to someone in the story or someone you know.
3. On the lines, write the name and address of the person who will get the card.
4. Turn the postcard over and draw a picture.

Lightning Strike!

Write a postcard for other books you read. Put them up on the bulletin board. Title the bulletin board: **"Book Places We Have Visited."**

Power Up!

- Show a postcard with a picture on one side and a message on the other.
- Explain that a book character could be a person, animal, or thing that the book tells about.
- Provide paper, crayons, and a pair of scissors for each group.

Name(s)_____

A WILD THING

Power Play

1. What would one more wild thing look like? Write down five words to describe how it would look.

    1. _____   4. _____

    2. _____   5. _____

    3. _____

2. Draw a picture of the wild thing to illustrate the words you wrote in step 1.

Lightning Strike!

Write a little play about the day that your wild thing met the other wild things in the book.

- -

Power Up!

- Read <u>Where the Wild Things Are</u> by Maurice Sendak (New York: Harper & Row, 1963).
- Provide each group with crayons.

WHAT IF?

Power Play

1. Pick two books you have read:

   1. _____

   2. _____

2. Pick a character from one book. Character:_____

3. Tell what would happen if that character went into the other book. _____

   _____

   _____

4. Draw a picture to show what would happen.

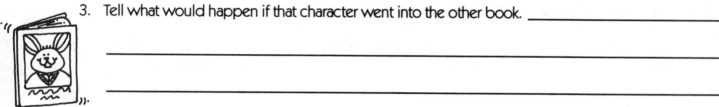

Lightning Strike!

1. Make a poster showing different book characters doing things together. Title the poster "What If?"
2. Write a totally new story with several of your favorite book characters together.

- -

Power Up!

- Provide a number of children's books with a variety of settings.
- Pick two of the books and ask the children to tell what it would be like for a character from one book to appear in the other one. For example, Amelia Bedelia in *Where the Wild Things Are.*

ONE IN A MILLION

Power Play

1. List the kind of cats you like.

_____   _____

_____   _____

_____   _____

2. What cat would you have picked if you were the man in the story? _____

3. Take turns naming the cats you like most.

    Your favorite cat:_____

    Why you like it the most: _____

4. Draw a picture of the cat you like most in the box below.
5. Share with one another the pictures of your favorite cats. Tell why you picked your cat.

```



```

Lightning Strike!
What if the man had looked for a dog or another animal? Repeat the cat activity using another animal.

Power Up!
• Read Millions of Cats by Wanda Gag (Putnam, 1996). Have the students describe the problem the old man had in selecting the right cat for the children.
• Provide crayons for each group.

WHERE AM I?

Power Play
1. Cut out the cards and mix them up. Lay them face down on the table.
2. Pick up a card and describe the word on the card without saying it. See if your partner can guess the word.
3. Take turns until you have guessed all the words.
4. Draw a picture on each card to match the word.

plains	**hill**	**lake**
river	**tropical island**	**ocean**
rain forest	**mountain**	**desert**

Lightning Strike!
1. Write down other words about land or water to describe and guess.
2. Draw different kinds of water or land on a poster.

Power Up!
- Review the following terms: *plains, hill, lake, river, tropical island, ocean, rain forest, mountain* and *desert*.
- Provide each group with a pair of scissors.

HELP THE HELPERS

Power Play
1. What do these community helpers need to do their jobs? Draw the things they need in the blank boxes beside them.
2. Cut out the helpers. Glue them to craft sticks.
3. Take turns acting out each helper's job.

Lightning Strike!
Draw and cut out other community helpers. Glue them to craft sticks. Act out stories about them.

Mail Carrier

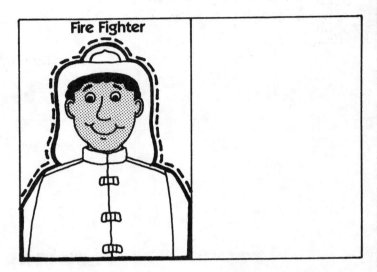

Fire Fighter

Librarian

Police Officer

- -

Power Up!
- Review the roles of the various community helpers illustrated above.
- Provide each group with crayons, scissors, glue, and craft sticks.

FROM ME TO YOU

Power Play

1. Cut out the mailbox and story strip. Cut out the dotted lines on each side of the mailbox.
2. Talk with your partner about what happens to a letter after it is mailed.
3. Decide on three or four steps to include on your story strip.
4. Draw the pictures to illustrate those steps.
5. Fit the strip through the mailbox.
6. Tell what is happening while you pull the story strip through the mailbox.

Lightning Strike!

Cut the pictures apart and make a book showing what happens to a letter.

Power Up!

- Review what happens to a letter between the time it is sent and the time it is delivered.
- Provide each group with crayons and scissors.

Name(s)_____

LIFE IN A LOG CABIN

Power Play

Abe Lincoln, like most pioneer children, grew up in a log cabin. These homes did not have electricity or running water. The fireplace provided heat and light to read.

1. Talk with your partner about what it would have been like to live in a log cabin.
2. List some ways living in a log cabin would be different from living in a modern house.

Lightning Strike!

1. Build your own log cabin out of Lincoln logs. Why do you think they were named Lincoln logs?
2. Read about Abe Lincoln and other people who lived in log cabins.
3. Draw a picture of yourself in a log cabin.

Power Up!

In this activity students compare living in a log cabin to living in their homes today. They consider how different life would be without the luxuries we take for granted, like television, indoor plumbing, telephones and computers. Provide picture books showing log cabins like the ones Lincoln and other pioneer children once lived in.

WAYS WE USE WATER

Power Play
1. Keep track of how you use water during one day. Fill in the chart each time you use water. Tell how you wasted any water.
2. Show your list to your partner. Answer these questions together:
   How did both of you save water?
   How did both of you waste water?
3. Turn the paper over. Make a list of other ways you both can save water.

How I Saved Water	How I Wasted Water

Lightning Strike!
1. Keep a record of water use for another day. See if you save more water this time.
2. Use your lists of ways to save water to make a giant "SAVE WATER" poster. Draw pictures of things a person could do to save water.

Power Up!
• Talk with the students about ways we use water in our everyday lives, some familiar ways to save water, and the need to conserve it.
• If need be, explain how to fill in the above chart.

SORT THE STAMPS

Power Play

1. Look at the stamps below.
2. What are some of the different ways you can group the stamps?

   _____

   _____

   _____

3. Fill out a table that tells the number of stamps in each group.

Kinds of Stamps	Number of Stamps

Lightning Strike!

1. Look for stamps that show people, places, nature, or animals that you have learned about in school.
2. Have your parents save all the stamps that come into your home for a week. Tape them onto a sheet of paper for a stamp collection.

- -

Power Up!

Sorting stamps encourages students to devise a variety of criteria for dividing objects into categories. Before beginning the activity, talk with them about possible classifications for stamps, including first-class stamps, postcard stamps, stamps with people, stamps with non-living things, stamps with no words, etc. Ask someone from a stamp club to visit the class and share his or her hobby.

Name(s)_____

STAMP SET

Power Play

1. Pick something you have studied in social studies that could be shown in a stamp set.

   _____

2. Decide the picture you will put on each stamp and how much postage each stamp will be worth.

Picture	Postage

3. Draw squares for stamps. Draw the picture on each stamp and show the postage.

Lightning Strike!

1. Make a class stamp book with the stamps made by each group.
2. Draw stamps on squares cut from pieces of colored construction paper.
3. Draw a large poster-sized version of one of your stamps.
4. Think of other ways people could pay to have their letters mailed.

Power Up!

Designing a stamp set can be a good way to apply social studies knowledge to a new situation.
- Show examples of stamps that are part of a set.
- Provide each group with fine felt-tipped markers or colored pencils.

NO MORE CHOCOLATE!

Power Play

What if it was against the law for anyone under 18 to eat chocolate? Pretend the governor wants to pass this law. Would this be a good law? Why or why not?

1. Talk about it with your partner. List your reasons below.

_____

_____

_____

_____

_____

2. On another piece of paper, write a letter to the governor telling how you feel about this law. Use the reasons you listed above to plan and organize your letter.

Lightning Strike!

Think about why we need laws. What would happen if there were no laws? Pick a law that you think is a good one. Tell what it is and why it is good.

Power Up!

Many writing activities like letters, reports, and stories require pre-planning and organization. After students list reasons why they would or would not agree with a law against chocolate, they are asked to organize those reasons into a letter format.

This activity could be used as an introduction to a discussion on how laws are made at the local, state, or national level. Other related topics are some examples of laws that have been changed and what people can do if they believe a law is wrong.

COUNT THE STARS

Power Play

1. Count the triangles. Color 1 triangle in the box for each triangle you counted.
2. Count the circles. Color 1 circle in the box for each circle you counted.
3. Count the stars. Color 1 star in the box for each star you counted.

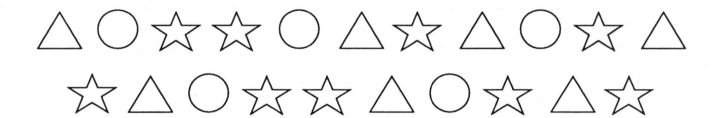

Triangles	△	△	△	△	△	△	△	△	△	△
Circles	○	○	○	○	○	○	○	○	○	○
Stars	☆	☆	☆	☆	☆	☆	☆	☆	☆	☆
	1	2	3	4	5	6	7	8	9	10

4. Are there more triangles, circles, or stars? _____

Lightning Strike!

Think of some other things you could count and show on a graph. How does a graph help you see which group of objects is the largest?

- -

Power Up!

Are there more stars, circles, or triangles? One way to find out is to make a graph. This activity introduces students to the idea of visually representing groups of objects or numbers on a graph. Show students other types of bar graphs. Explain how the longest bar represents the largest number.

BIKE HIKE

Power Play

Tasha and Nick went on a bike ride around the lake. Look at the map below to see where they went.

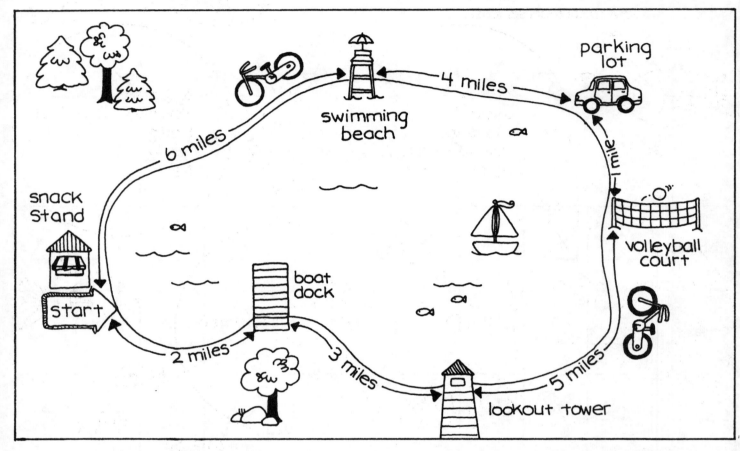

1. With your partner, write five math questions that could be answered by looking at the map. The questions could involve addition, subtraction, multiplication, division, or a combination of two or more.
2. Give your questions to another group to solve.

Lightning Strike!

Draw your own map. Take turns with your partner asking number questions about it.

- -

Power Up!

In this activity, students practice writing their own story problems. Explain how to read the map shown above. Give students one example to help them get started: If Tasha and Nick rode 1 mile in 15 minutes, how long did it take them to get to the boat dock?

WHAT'S THE PROBLEM?

Power Play
1. Read the information in each circle.
2. Underline the problem in each story.
3. Write a number sentence for each problem.
4. Solve the number sentence.

Fish tank
5 goldfish
10 guppies
How many fish in all?
Right after dinner

Jungle gym
How many children in all?
5 boys
4 o'clock
6 girls

How many more runs did
the blue team have?
Ball game
10 runs for the blue team
5 runs for the red team
April 23

Bus ride
20 children
How many boys were on
the bus?
10 girls
10 miles

Lightning Strike!
Write number stories for your partner to solve.

Power Up!
To solve a problem students need to know what the problem is. Demonstrate how to underline the problem, then solve it with a number sentence.

Example: 1 red bird
3 black birds
<u>How many birds in the tree?</u>
$1 + 3 = 4$

FS112111 POWERTHINK   Frank Schaffer Publications

PICTURE IT!

Power Play

Draw your own pictures to solve these word problems.

1. Mary has 8 checkers. She loses 2 checkers. How many checkers are left?

2. Jesse has 5 marbles on the game board. She moves 2 marbles off the board. How many marbles are left?

3. Tom caught 3 fish. He catches 4 more fish. Now how many fish does Tom have?

Lightning Strike!

1. Make up number stories for your partner to draw pictures for and solve.
2. Draw pictures. Make up number stories to go with them.

Power Up!

Explain that drawing pictures is one way to solve a problem. Show how to draw a picture to solve a problem: Nick has 7 cards. He puts 2 down. How many cards are left?

$7 - 2 = 5$

I get it!

FS112111 POWERTHINK

MAGIC CIRCLES

Power Play

1. Write a number in the center of the magic circle.

2. Write numbers in two more circles along one line.
   Add the numbers.

3. What two numbers can you put in the other two circles to make the
   same total for that line? Write them in.

4. See how many more magic circles you can make.

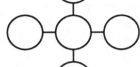

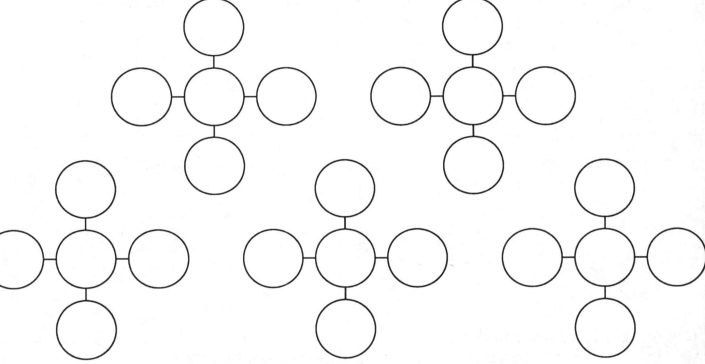

Lightning Strike!

Try this with more than five circles.
Use one of these patterns or make up your own.

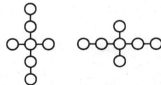

Power Up!

Demonstrate how to fill in both directions of the magic circle
with numbers that add up to the same sum in each direction.

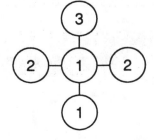

THE HIDDEN TRIANGLE

Power Play

1. Look at this triangle.
2. Find it in each picture and color it in.

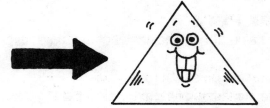

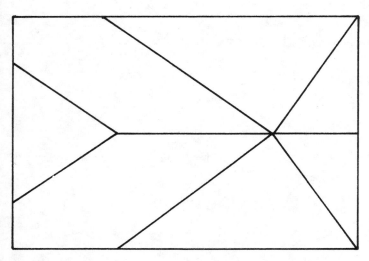

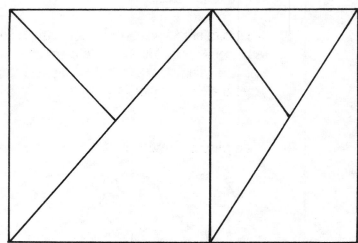

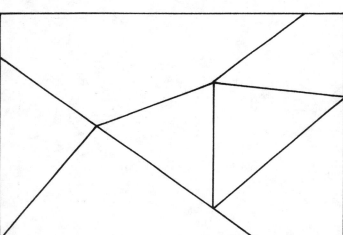

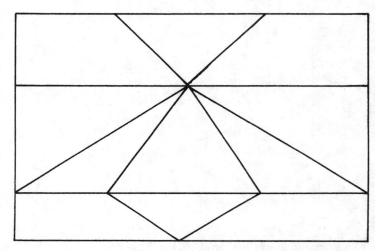

Lightning Strike!

Cut out a shape. Trace it onto another piece of paper. Draw more lines to hide it. See if your partner can find and color the hidden shape.

Power Up!

Learning to compare characteristics such as shape and size is an important critical thinking skill. This exercise challenges the student to compare and find the matching triangle in each diagram.

• Provide crayons for each group.

THE PARTS MAKE THE WHOLE

Power Play

When you make a puzzle, you look at the shape of the missing piece. Then you try to find a piece that matches.

1. Look at the pieces below. Think about how they could fit together.
2. Write the letters of the pieces needed to make each shape.

What pieces do you need to make this triangle? ____ ____ ____

What pieces do you need to make this square? ____ ____ ____

What pieces do you need to make this circle? ____ ____ ____

A B C D E F G H I

Lightning Strike!

How is this activity like making a puzzle? Would it be easier if you could pick up the pieces and try them in different places? Why?

Take a sheet of paper. Draw a large shape on it. Cut out the shape. Then cut the shape into three or more pieces for your partner to put together.

Power Up!

It is more difficult to solve a puzzle when you cannot pick up the pieces and try them. Students learn to visualize the whole and determine how the parts go together to make the whole.

Answers: △ = A, E, I; □ = C, F, H; ○ = B, D, G.

WHO READ WHAT?

Power Play

1. Jill read 4 books.
   Tom read 3 books.
   Latosha read 5 books.
   Two of the children read a total of 8 books. Who are they? _____ and _____
2. Use "guess and check" to find the answer. Here's how:
3. Write number sentences for the books read by:

   Jill and Tom: _____

   Jill and Latosha: _____

   Tom and Latosha: _____

4. Now, go back and write the names of the two children who read 8 books in the blank spaces above.

Jill  Tom  Latosha

Lightning Strike!

Sara has $.42. Eric has $.54. Kelly has $.14 more than Sara. They want to buy a kite that costs $.96. Which two children could put their money together and have exactly the right amount of money?

- -

Power Up!

Learning to see how parts come together to make a whole is an important part of deductive reasoning. This activity also introduces the concept of "guess and check," an important strategy for problem solving.

IT'S ABOUT TIME!

Power Play

1. Lee has a digital watch. Sarah has a watch with hands that move. Which kind do you like best?
2. With your partner, make a chart to compare the two kinds of watches.

Digital Watch		**Watch with Hands**	
Advantages	Disadvantages	Advantages	Disadvantages
_____	_____	_____	_____
_____	_____	_____	_____
_____	_____	_____	_____
_____	_____	_____	_____
_____	_____	_____	_____

3. Look over your lists. Which kind of watch do you want? _____

   Why? _____

4. Share your answer with your partner.

Lightning Strike!

Think about a gas lawn mower and a push mower. Which costs more? Which is easier to use? Which is better for the environment? Write some advantages and disadvantages for each.

- -

Power Up!

An important thinking skill is the ability to methodically analyze options, and then choose the best one. In this exercise the children are encouraged to look at two ways of measuring time in order to decide which they like to use best.

- Review the ways that a digital clock and a clock with hands tell time.
- Explain the process of looking for the advantages and disadvantages of two or more options.

Name(s)_____

TREE TALK

Power Play
1. Take turns telling some things you know about trees.
2. What do you think a tree would want to tell about itself? Write what it would say on each branch.
3. Color the picture.

Lightning Strike!
1. Make a picture of a different kind of growing thing (like a flower, a bush, or a Christmas tree).
2. On your picture, write words to describe what it might tell about itself.

- -

Power Up!
- Discuss parts of a tree and their functions, as well as how a tree changes during the seasons and from year to year.
- Provide crayons for each group.

PEEK IN A PEANUT

Power Play

1. Open the peanut shell. Draw a picture of what you see inside.

2. Open one of the peanuts. Look for the seed inside it. Draw a picture of the seed.

3. Think about what you saw and what you know about seeds and plants. Answer these questions.

Why is the peanut shell hard? _____

_____

When a peanut is planted, what will happen to the seed inside it?_____

_____

Lightning Strike!

Read a book about peanuts. Plant a raw peanut to find out what happens after it is planted. Draw pictures to show how the peanut plant grows. When the plant is fully grown, where are the peanuts?

- -

Power Up!

- Review how plants grow from seeds.
- Provide each group with crayons and a peanut in the shell. Explain that even though the peanut has been roasted, the seed inside can still be seen.
- Provide several extra peanuts for eating.

Name(s)_____

FIRST AID FOR FROSTY!

 Power Play
Help! Frosty's melting!
Brainstorm with your partner. In the space below list as many ways as
you can think of to keep poor Frosty from a fatal meltdown.
The sky's the limit, so use your imagination!

```
_____

_____

_____

_____

_____

_____

_____

_____
```

 Lightning Strike!
Look at each of your ideas to save Frosty. Put a star by the one you think is best. Write more information
about how this idea could work. Draw a picture explaining your idea.

- -

 Power Up!
Children's curiosity and imagination make them natural scientists. Just as we would never attempt
to restrict the thinking of a scientist, we should provide opportunities in the classroom for
unrestricted brainstorming.

MIXED-UP BEANS

 Power Play

1. Seeds come in many sizes and colors. Take the seeds out of the bag and look at them. See if you know what kind of plant they came from.
2. Sort the bean seeds into different piles.
3. Fill in the chart to show how many beans are in each group.

Kind of Beans	Number of Beans
_____	_____
_____	_____
_____	_____
_____	_____
_____	_____
_____	_____
_____	_____
_____	_____

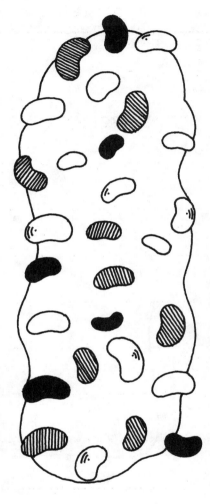

 Lightning Strike!

1. Show other ways beans can be sorted.
2. Glue each bean onto poster board. Label it. Above each bean draw a picture of the plant that grows from it.
3. Use library books to help identify the types of seeds.

- -

 Power Up!

- Demonstrate how to write the name and number of things we count in a simple table.
- Gently encourage students to categorize beans according to criteria such as shape, size, texture, color, and whether or not it easily splits in half.
- Provide each group with a bag containing about 25 beans. Take them from a bag of mixed beans.

DESIGN A PLANT

Power Play

1. Pretend you are scientists making a new kind of plant. What kind of plant will you make?

_____

2. What kind of seed will your plant have? Draw a picture.

3. What kind of flower will your plant have? Draw a picture.

4. What will your plant look like when grown? Draw a picture.

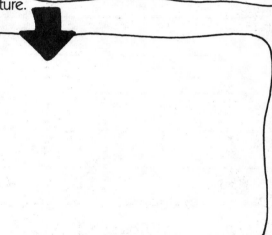

5. What will your plant be used for? _____

_____

Lightning Strike!

Share your new plant with the rest of the class. Try to think of more ways that your plant could be used.

- -

Power Up!

- Explain how scientists are using genetic engineering to make new kinds of plants.
- Provide each group with crayons. As an option, also provide construction paper, scissors, and glue.

WHAT DO YOU SEE?

Power Play

To **observe** means to look at what is around you and *really* see what is there.
Study the picture below for two minutes. Look closely at everything. Your teacher will ask you questions about what you observed. When the time is up, turn this page over.

Lightning Strike!

Are you a good observer? Without looking, what color socks are you wearing? What colors is the person behind you wearing? Does your teacher wear a watch? On the right hand or left? Describe the shoes your teacher is wearing today. Practice being an observer. Look around a room, then close your eyes and see how much you can remember.

- -

Power Up!

People look, but they do not see. After the students have studied the picture for two minutes, ask them to turn the page over and answer questions about the picture. When they have finished, have them look at the picture again and check their answers. What fruits are in the picture? What time is it? How many children are in the picture? What is the cat looking at? What items are in the shopping cart? What pattern is on the floor? How many flowers are on the woman's hat? (The woman isn't wearing a hat.) What does the large poster under the clock say? How many pumpkins are shown? Ask at least one question that isn't answered by the picture: How much do the apples cost?

DRAW A POEM

Power Play

1. Listen to the poem as your teacher reads it.
2. What images come to mind?
3. Draw a picture to illustrate this poem.

Lightning Strike!

1. Look at the other drawings. Notice the differences in the drawings for the same poem. Select the drawing you like best and tell the person why you like it.
2. Select a different poem that you enjoy. Draw a picture for that poem. Display your drawings in the classroom.
3. Write a poem of your own and draw a picture for it.

- -

Power Up!

Read the poem "Fog" by Carl Sandburg or select another short poem you think the students would enjoy. Read the poem through several times slowly. Ask students to close their eyes as they listen carefully to the poem. Write the poem on the blackboard.

- Provide crayons, markers, and paper for the students.

SHAPE MOBILES

Power Play

1. Look around your classroom. What shapes do you see? Pick one of those shapes for this activity.
2. Draw and cut the shape out of paper.
3. Draw a line around the inside of the shape to its middle.
   Follow the sides of the shape as you do this.
4. Use markers to decorate the inside of the shape.
5. Cut along the line you drew in the shape.
6. Punch a hole in the center of the shape.
7. Tie a piece of yarn through the shape and hang it up.

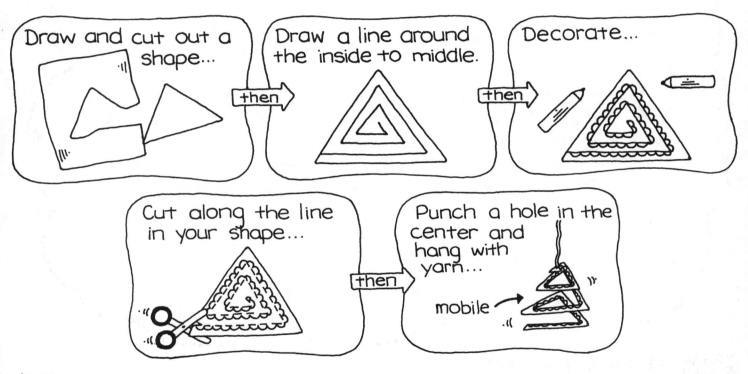

Lightning Strike!

Pick several shapes to cut out and hang on a coat hanger for a "Shape Mobile."

- -

Power Up!

Cutting hanging mobiles from shapes provides students with a chance to apply something they have learned to another area.

- Review different shapes the class has studied. Discuss the different shapes found in your classroom.
- Provide each group with construction paper, scissors, a piece of yarn, a straight edge, a hole punch, and markers.

WHAT COLOR IS A GIGGLE?

Power Play

1. What color do you think a giggle would be? _____
2. Draw a giggle and color it.

3. Pick one of these words: lonely, proud, sad, happy.
4. What color does the word make you think of? Draw a picture for the word you picked.

Lightning Strike!

Think of other words that are not objects. List the words and the colors you think they might be.

Power Up!

Ask students to explain what it means to feel "blue." Name other colors and have them think of feelings to match the colors. Talk about how colors and feelings are related.

AT THE END OF THE RAINBOW

Power Play

Nancee and Mike found a pot at the end of the rainbow.

1. What do you think might be in this magic pot?
2. Draw something in the pot that Nancee and Mike might have found. Color the rainbow.

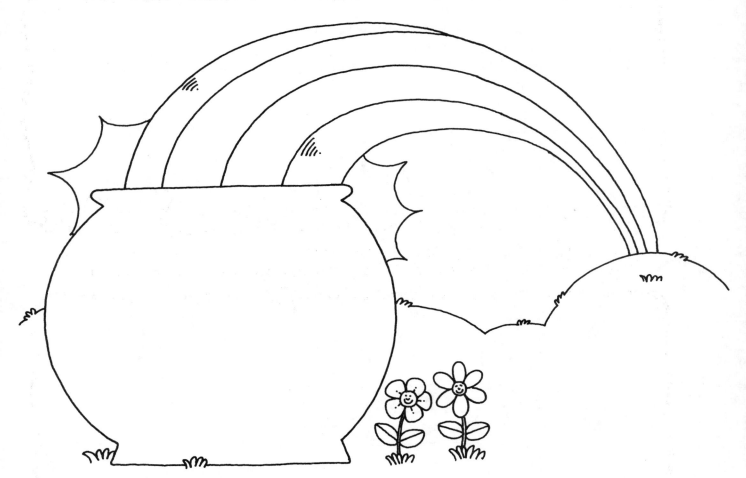

Lightning Strike!

1. What other great things would you like to find in a pot at the end of the rainbow? What would be the best thing to find? Why?
2. Use long strips of colored paper or streamers to make a rainbow on the bulletin board. Cut out your pot and put it at the end of the rainbow.

Power Up!

In this activity students predict what Nancee and Mike might have found in a pot at the end of a rainbow. Then they are asked to make a value judgement by thinking of the best thing someone could find.

- Ask several students to describe what they drew in the pot and why that would be good to find.

PUTTING IT ALL TOGETHER

Power Play
A collage is made up of pictures and words. Sometimes all the pictures and words are about one idea called a theme.
1. Look at pictures in the magazines.
2. With a partner, decide on a theme.
3. Cut out pictures and words about the theme you picked.
4. Decide how to arrange them before you glue.
5. Glue the pictures and words to a piece of paper so the whole page is covered. Some pictures can be partly over other ones.

Lightning Strike!
1. Look at the other collages your classmates made. See if you can figure out what themes they used.
2. Make a collage out of colored pieces of paper in different sizes and shapes. How is a collage like a patchwork quilt?

- -

Power Up!
Making a collage from magazine pictures provides a "hands-on" way to practice synthesis, by combining different shapes and colors.
- Explain what the word "theme" means. Some ideas for themes could be transportation, plants, recreation, seasons, lakes, inventions, animals, happiness, and family. Ask students to suggest other themes. Show them an example of a theme collage.
- Provide scissors, glue, paper, and lots of magazines.

ZOO SHAPE

Power Play
1. Pick a shape.
2. Think about how you can use that shape to make a zoo animal.
3. Draw the shape onto paper and cut it out.
4. Cut out other shapes needed to make the animal.
5. Glue your animal together.
6. Add details with a crayon.

Think of how a shape could be part of a zoo animal.

→then→ Cut out that shape and the other pieces that you need to make your animal...

head neck rectangle (body)

tail → legs →

Glue everything together.

→then→ Draw and color on details!

Hey—that turned out great!

Lightning Strike!
1. Make up a new animal.
2. Glue yarn and other scrap materials onto your animal.
3. Put all the animals together to make a class zoo.

Power Up!
To most of us, the natural world is irregular: lumpy, fuzzy, curved, and jagged. But with a little practice, children can learn to reduce animals and other natural objects to their basic forms, such as squares, circles, spheres, cubes, cones and cylinders. The idea is to explore the links between two distinct bodies of knowledge: geometry and animal structure.
- Before beginning, review shapes recently studied in class, and provide each group with construction paper, scissors, glue, and crayons.

WHAT'S ON THE LIST?

Power Play

1. A list is a useful way to help you remember things. People make lists when they go grocery shopping. What other types of lists could people make? Write some types below.

_____

_____

_____

2. What kind of a list could you make? _____
    What things would be on your list? Write them on the list.

_____'s List

_____   _____

_____   _____

_____   _____

_____   _____

_____   _____

_____   _____

groceries
apples
oranges
lettuce
ketchup
cake
muffins

Lightning Strike!

1. How is writing things on a calendar like making a list? How would a list be useful to a baseball coach? What kind of list would a teacher make?
2. Make a list of books you'd like to read or places you'd like to visit. Write your lists in a small notebook. Carry it with you when you go to the library.

- -

Power Up!

Students need to learn various ways to organize their thoughts and actions. Making a written list is another method of organization students can use at an early age.

WHAT A MESS!

Power Play

Do you ever have a messy room?

1. Write about what makes your room messy.
2. For each cause, figure out what you can do about it.

What makes my room messy	What I can do about it

Lightning Strike!

1. Make a chart showing what you will do each day to keep your room clean.
2. With a partner, write a list telling ways you can clean up your school grounds or classroom.

Power Up!

Identifying problems and listing the causes and some possible solutions is an effective approach to problem solving. This exercise shows how such an approach can help with the ongoing problem of a messy room.

- Explain that one way to solve a problem is to first list the problem's causes, followed by ways to solve it.

THANK-YOU CARD

Power Play

1. Think of a gift you have received.
2. Get ready to write a thank-you note by answering the following questions about your gift.

Who? _____

When? _____

Where? _____

What? _____

Why? _____

3. Use your answers to fill in the blanks in this letter.

Dear (who?)_____,

Thank you very much for (what?)_____which you gave me on

(when?)_____at (where?)_____

for (why?)_____.

    Thanks again,

    (Your name)_____

4. Have your partner read your letter and look for any mistakes.
5. Write the letter neatly on a note card.
6. Send or deliver your letter to the person who gave you the gift.

Lightning Strike!
Use *who, when, where, what* and *why* to plan and write an invitation to a party.

Power Up!
The questions *who, when, where, what* and *why* are useful for analyzing stories. They can also provide a useful organizational structure for writing a thank-you card, a letter, or a book report.

• Provide note cards for each group.

HOW DO YOU FEEL?

Power Play

1. Happy, sad, and lonely are kinds of feelings. List some other feelings you have.

_____

_____

_____

_____

2. One way to explain a word is to give an example. Sad is how you feel when your best friend moves away. Finish these sentences to explain your feelings.

A. Sad is how you feel when _____

_____

B. Jealous is how you feel when _____

_____

C. Lonely is how you feel when _____

_____

D. Proud is how you feel when _____

_____

E. Happy is how you feel when _____

_____

Lightning Strike!

Think of some things you can do when you feel sad, lonely or jealous to make yourself feel better. How can you help your friends or family members when they are sad?

- -

Power Up!

Definition by example is one way to help students understand a word better.

• Ask students to suggest several endings to this sentence: Rejected is how you feel when…

WHAT COMES NEXT?

 Power Play

When faced with a task, it often helps to stop and think before you start. Think about the steps to be done and the order in which to do them.

1. Look at the pictures in the boxes. Decide which one should come first, second, third, and so on. Write the number under the box.

_____ _____ _____ _____ _____ _____

2. Select another task. Write it here: _____
3. Think of the steps needed to do that task. Write them on another piece of paper. Draw each step in order in the boxes below.

     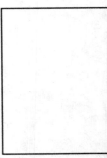

 Lightning Strike!

How can thinking about the steps help you organize a task? What are some advantages of taking time to write out the steps before you begin?

- -

 Power Up!

Verbalizing, writing, and illustrating the steps needed to complete a task are all ways to assist students in organizing their thoughts and actions.

FS112111 POWERTHINK

BUY, BUILD, OR MAKE?

Power Play
1. Look at each kind of bird feeder.
2. Write one good thing and one bad thing about each kind of bird feeder.

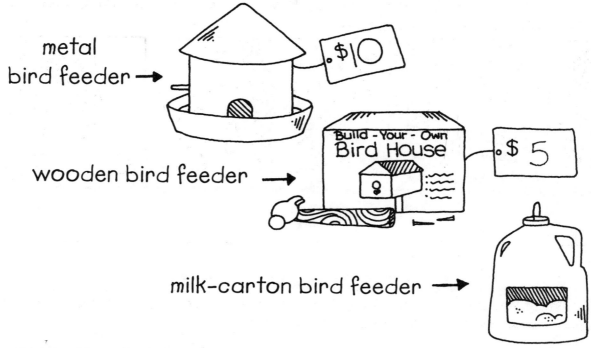

metal bird feeder → $10

wooden bird feeder →   Build-Your-Own Bird House $5

milk-carton bird feeder →

3. Which bird feeder do you think Jasmine should choose? Circle the answer.

metal bird feeder   wooden bird feeder   milk-carton bird feeder

4. Why? _____

5. Turn the paper over and draw a picture of Jasmine with the bird feeder you think she should have.

Lightning Strike!
Think of a decision you have to make with two or more possible choices. Write the good and bad things about each one.

- -

Power Up!
One way to make a choice is to list the pros and cons of each option.
- Read the following passage to the students: "Jasmine wants a bird feeder. She knows of three ways to get one. She can buy a metal bird feeder for $10. She can buy a wooden kit to put together for $5. She can make a bird feeder from an empty plastic milk carton she already has. Help her decide what to do."
- Provide each group with crayons.

FLOWER BOX SURPRISE

Power Play

1. Juan wants to put six plants in a row in the flower box. He can pick from plants that are red, white, pink, yellow, and purple. Help Juan pick the plants to go in the flower box.
2. Draw pictures of some of the different ways Juan could put six plants into the box.

3. Choose what you think is the best way to put the flowers in the box. Draw the flowers in Juan's flower box.

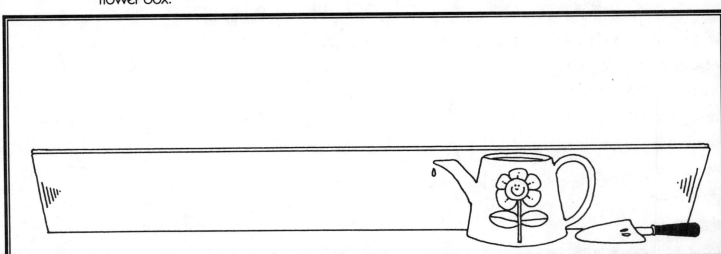

4. Show your drawing to your partner. Tell why you planted the flower box in this way.

Lightning Strike!

1. Draw a flower box for your home. Draw some flowers that you would like to plant in it.
2. Draw a plan for a flower garden in a park in your neighborhood. Show how the different colored flowers would be arranged in your garden.

- -

Power Up!

Drawing a picture is a useful problem-solving strategy.

- Read the following passage to the students: "Juan's mother is letting him plant flowers in the flower box on the front porch. He may pick six petunias from several boxes of bedding plants that she bought at a greenhouse. She has red, white, pink, yellow, and purple petunias. Help Juan decide which petunias to put in the flower box."
- Provide each group with crayons.